GLOUCESTER DO

AN HISTORICAL GUIDE

Hugh Conway-Jones

THE DOCKS. GLOUCESTER.   123.

Black Dwarf
Publications

A sketch of the docks, from a guide to Gloucester c.1930.

Published by
**BLACK DWARF
PUBLICATIONS**

© Black Dwarf Publications &
Hugh Conway-Jones 2009
Designed by Neil Parkhouse

British Library Cataloguing-in-Publication
Data. A catalogue record for this book is
available from the British Library

ISBN 13: 9781903599 15 0

**BLACK DWARF LIGHTMOOR
PUBLICATIONS LTD**
Unit 144B, Lydney Trading Estate,
Harbour Road, Lydney, Gloucestershire
GL15 5EJ

www.lightmoor.co.uk

*Black Dwarf Publications is an imprint of
Black Dwarf Lightmoor Publications Ltd*

Printed & bound by
Information Press, Eynsham, Oxford

CONTENTS

Bringing Ships to Gloucester	page 3
Early Use of the Basin	page 4
Development of the Docks	page 5
Changes in Traffic	page 6
Final Phase of Commercial Traffic	page 7
The Warehouses	page 8
Main Docks Buildings and Plan	page 10
Main Basin	page 12
North Warehouse	page 14
Around the North Quay	page 15
East Quay Warehouses	page 16
Southern Warehouses	page 17
Western Warehouses	page 18
Docks From the Air	page 19
Gloucester Lock	page 20
Riverside Quay	page 21
Dry Docks	page 22
Engine House	page 23
Victoria Dock	page 24
Pridays Mill	page 25
Around the Victoria Dock	page 26
Mariners Chapel	page 27
Tramroad	page 28
Railways	page 29
1902 OS Map	page 30
The Barge Arm	page 31
Llanthony Bridge	page 32
South of Llanthony Bridge	page 33
Bakers Quay	page 34
Buildings on Bakers Quay	page 35
Llanthony Quay	page 36
South of High Orchard Bridge	page 37
Handling Grain	page 38
Handling Timber	page 40
Dock Labourers	page 42
Seamen	page 43
Boatmen	page 44
Bargemen	page 45
A New Era	page 46

Acknowledgements

I would like to record my thanks to those organisations who have provided illustrations, particularly Gloucestershire Archives, The Waterways Trust, English Heritage NMR and Gloucester City Museums. I am also grateful to Neil Parkhouse for access to his postcard collection, to Philip Moss for two of his fine drawings, to Paul Barnett for access to the Graham Farr collection, to Ben Ashworth for a railway photograph, to Ian Pope for providing the maps, to Michael Keen-Price for the peanuts story, to Dr Ray Wilson for commenting on the draft and to my wife Rosemary for much practical help. All uncredited illustrations are the author's. This book draws on the research carried out for my *Gloucester Docks – An Illustrated History* (1984), where sources are quoted. *Hugh Conway-Jones, Gloucester 2009*

Bringing Ships to Gloucester

The seal of the Gloucester & Berkeley Canal Company, drawn by Philip Moss from surviving share certificates.

For hundreds of years, the River Severn provided an important trade route between the Midlands and the great port of Bristol, and many types of cargoes were carried in both directions by shallow draught sailing vessels. In 1580, Gloucester was given the formal status of a customs port by a charter from Queen Elizabeth I and a custom house was built adjoining the riverside Quay. However, few seagoing ships came up to Gloucester, because of the difficulty of navigating the narrow winding river approaching the city, whilst even local vessels could only pass this stretch during a few days each fortnight at the time of spring tides. During the 18th century, there was a considerable growth in trade on the river and this led to a proposal to construct a ship canal between Gloucester and Berkeley Pill. The canal would not only allow through traffic to avoid the worst part of the river, it would also help to develop the port of Gloucester as a rival to Bristol.

The Gloucester & Berkeley Canal was authorised by Act of Parliament in 1793 and work started at the Gloucester end under the direction of Robert Mylne. Constructing a ship canal was a mammoth undertaking for its time and the project was beset by financial and management difficulties. In fact work had to stop in 1799, as most of the original share capital had been spent, although the digging had only progressed as far as Hardwicke, about five miles from Gloucester.

For the next few years, there was much discussion about how the canal could be completed but it was not possible to raise the necessary money. In 1812, however, the lock at Gloucester was brought into operation so that river craft could use the basin for transferring cargoes – a move which particularly suited a new horse-operated tramroad to Cheltenham. Then the Canal Company agreed to adopt a new line for the canal, joining the Severn at Sharpness Point, sixteen miles from Gloucester, and with financial support from the Exchequer Bill Loan Commissioners, work started again in 1817. At this stage, the project came under the general supervision of Thomas Telford, acting as consultant engineer to the Loan Commissioners. After good initial progress, including a junction with the Stroudwater Canal in 1820, construction was again delayed by financial and management difficulties. Then in 1823, Telford brought in the experienced contractor Hugh McIntosh who worked under the supervision of resident engineer Thomas Fletcher and eventually completed the canal in 1827. During this final phase, a Barge Arm was constructed at Gloucester to ensure that the Main Basin could be kept free for sea-going ships.

Map of the ship canal between Gloucester and Sharpness.

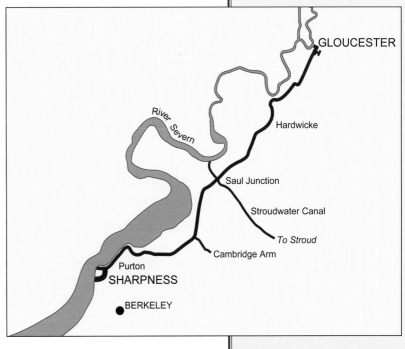

Early Use of the Basin

Trows in the basin at Gloucester
c.1823.
GLOUCESTERSHIRE ARCHIVES

The canal was formally opened on the 26th April 1827, when a huge crowd gathered to watch the first two vessels enter the basin amid the firing of guns and the ringing of church bells. Some spectators watched from the vantage point of the large pair of semi-detached warehouses built by the Canal Company on the North Quay. With the canal fully operational, merchants soon took advantage of the new facilities. Importing through Gloucester cut out the former need for transhipment at Bristol, where there were high port charges. Imported cargoes could be transferred direct to narrow canal boats, which could carry the goods up the river and through the inland canal network to supply the growing industrial towns of the Midlands.

The geographical position of Gloucester so far inland was a tremendous advantage and traffic was soon exceeding all expectations. As well as the vessels employed in the river trade, there were increasing numbers of single-masted sloops, two-masted brigs and schooners, and some three-masted barques. Early imports included corn from Ireland and mainland Europe, timber from the Baltic and North America, and wines and spirits from Portugal and France. The main export was salt, which was brought down the river from Worcestershire, although many ships, after unloading, went to one of the South Wales ports to load coal.

As trade developed, more warehouses were built around the basin, an earlier dry dock was enlarged and an engine house was built to augment the canal's water supply by pumping from the River Severn. To extend the quay space, Bakers Quay was constructed to the south of Llanthony Bridge.

Llanthony Bridge and Bakers Quay in 1843. Beyond Llanthony Bridge can be seen the warehouses around the Main Basin, with the cathedral in the background. Bakers Quay on the right was financed by a group of merchants led by Samuel Baker, who had made money through owning slave plantations in Jamaica. The Pillar Warehouse was built for storing corn and the rest of the quay was originally laid out for timber yards. Several of these yards were surrounded by high fences and were locked up under customs supervision, so that foreign timber could be stored there without paying import duty until it was sold to a customer.
GLOUCESTERSHIRE ARCHIVES

Development of the Docks

During the 1840s, it was realised that further developments would be necessary. At busy times, the basin became so crowded that vessels had to wait their turn for a berth. Also, there was a national movement towards reduced import duties, particularly the repeal of the Corn Laws in 1846, and the Canal Company recognised they should prepare for a major increase in foreign imports. They therefore arranged for the Victoria Dock to be constructed, to the east of the Main Basin with a narrow cut linking the two, and the new dock was opened in 1849.

Also during the 1840s, there were various moves to bring railway connections into the docks. Initially, improvements were made to the existing horse-operated Gloucester & Cheltenham Tramroad but this was still unsatisfactory due to its narrow gauge and sharp bends. Then the Midland Railway constructed a standard gauge line from their station to the south end of Bakers Quay, with a branch serving the east side of the main docks area. A few years later, the Gloucester & Dean Forest Railway built a broad gauge branch from the South Wales line to serve a new quay on the west side of the canal and this was operated by the Great Western Railway. These lines were increasingly used to distribute imports to the Midlands in competition with the river and canal route.

With the benefit of the improved facilities, foreign imports increased dramatically during the 1850s and 60s. Corn came from northern Europe and the Black Sea ports situated around the mouth of the Danube. More warehouses were constructed and three flour mills were established. Timber came from the Baltic, North America and the arctic coast of Russia, and new timber yards and saw mills were established beside the canal south of Gloucester. Some of the vessels bringing timber from North America were locally owned and they often carried emigrants on the outward journey. Other imports included wines and spirits, oranges and lemons, and bones and guano for fertiliser. Unfortunately, salt was still the only regular export and most vessels had to go elsewhere to find a return cargo.

A view of the Main Basin in 1876. The large ships would have had to transfer some of their cargo into lighters at Sharpness, in order to reduce their draught to suit the depth of water in the canal. The passenger steamer in the foreground was either WAVE or LAPWING, which ran regular services along the canal, carrying Gloucester people for business or a day out at Sharpness and bringing canal-side villagers to shop in Gloucester. In the middle of the basin can be seen a well-loaded canal boat and a steam barge.
NEIL PARKHOUSE

Changes in Traffic

During the 1860s, difficulties were reported because the general increase in the size of merchant ships meant that some were too big to come up the canal fully laden. After much deliberation, therefore, the Canal Company built a new entrance and dock at Sharpness that would take the largest ships of the day. The new dock opened in 1874 and this allowed the growth in imports to continue. Smaller vessels came up the canal as before, whilst cargoes from the larger ships were transhipped at Sharpness and brought up the canal in barges and lighters towed by tugs. Also in the 1870s, the Canal Company changed its name to the Sharpness New Dock & Gloucester & Birmingham Navigation Company, usually known as the Dock Company.

In the 1880s, the docks were being used by steamers as well as by sailing vessels and there were regular services from mainland Europe. In the 1890s, Monk Meadow Dock was built as an arm off the canal about half a mile south of the main docks area and it was used initially for the timber trade.

The docks remained busy through the early years of the 20th century but the First World War had a disastrous effect on the trade of the port. Half of the grain imports were lost due to the closing of the Black Sea to trade, and both the timber imports from the Baltic and the steamer trade with mainland Europe ceased altogether.

During the 1920s, the traditional imports of grain and timber recovered slowly but the warehouses at Gloucester remained underused, as much of the grain coming up the canal was carried in barges that continued on up the river. In the 1930s, a new traffic developed to meet the demand for petroleum products, for the growing number of road vehicles with internal combustion engines. This became very important in the years following and a fleet of tanker barges brought the petroleum from Avonmouth to Monk Meadow Dock, with some continuing up the River Severn to depots at Worcester and Stourport. However, the growth in road transport brought to an end the operation of the two passenger steamers which had provided a regular service along the canal since the 1850s.

A busy scene below Llanthony Bridge c.1913. The steam tug MOSS ROSE (left) is preparing to pick up a tow to Sharpness, which will probably include the loaded canal boats moored by the Pillar Warehouse. Behind the tug, men are transferring timber from a lighter to a canal boat. Meanwhile, the motor barge OSRIC is setting off for Avonmouth towing the dumb barge TOGO, both owned by the Severn & Canal Carrying Co. In the distance can be seen a barque in the Main Basin.
THE WATERWAYS TRUST

Final Phase of Commercial Traffic

During the Second World War, the west coast ports had to deal with additional ships diverted from London, and the canal and docks played a vital role in handling essential cargoes for the Midlands, particularly petroleum, metals, grain and other foodstuffs transhipped into barges at Avonmouth. The barge crews worked long hours to keep the supplies moving and they received extra rations as they were classed as merchant seamen. Some of the warehouses were brought back into use for storing grain as part of a strategic reserve and a large silo was built near Monk Meadow Dock for drying and storing home-grown grain.

After the war, the Dock Company was nationalised, and the canal and docks were taken over by what became British Waterways. The canal remained busy with barge traffic, and the new management set about improving the canal and its facilities to encourage more sea-going ships to come up to Gloucester. Coasters became a regular sight in the Main Basin and some use was made of the warehouses, although they were not really suitable for modern warehouse operations. In 1961, Llanthony Quay was refurbished for landing cargoes destined for onward transport by road and two large transit sheds were built, with floors at ground level suitable for vehicular access. Four years later, Monk Meadow Quay was constructed on the west bank of the canal. These improvements attracted one or two small coasters a week, bringing cargoes such as fertiliser, granite sets, grain and timber. The berths around the main docks area gradually went out of use and some of the warehouses were rented to non-waterway related businesses or just left empty.

During the 1960s, the barge traffic declined as petroleum was brought by coastal tanker to a new depot at Quedgeley (and occasionally to Monk Meadow Dock), whilst timber was also delivered to Gloucester by coaster. Most other cargoes changed to road transport, although a few barges still carried grain to Healing's mill at Tewkesbury. By the 1980s, coaster traffic was also declining due to competition from other ports and it effectively finished in 1988. This left the only remaining commercial traffic on the canal as the grain barges passing through to Tewkesbury, until these too came to an end in 1998.

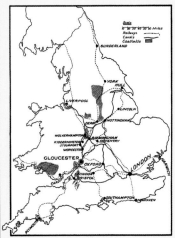

ABOVE: The inland port of Gloucester and its waterways connections to the Midlands manufacturing areas, c. 1925.

BELOW LEFT: Two coasters, the ANNA ELIZABETH of Amsterdam, left, and TYNEHAVEN of Newcastle discharging cargoes in the Main Basin in 1957. In the foreground, the British Waterways barge SEVERN FALCON is moored alongside a lighter laden with timber transhipped at Sharpness. THE WATERWAYS TRUST

BELOW: Llanthony Bridge is raised to let the motor barge CHACELEY depart Gloucester en route to collect wheat from Avonmouth in 1977.

The Warehouses

A manually-operated winch in the loft of Llanthony Warehouse.

One of the original drawings for Llanthony Warehouse dated 1873.
GLOUCESTERSHIRE ARCHIVES

The warehouses are major features in the landscape of the docks and they are reminders of the huge quantities of corn that passed through Gloucester on the way to the Midlands. Wheat, oats, barley, maize, beans and peas were stored in sacks until being sent on to a customer. It is estimated that the throughput was enough to fill and empty all of the warehouses three or four times every year. Although they were built for a variety of different owners over a period of almost fifty years, they are remarkably similar in design. This uniformity was partly due to the Canal Company imposing conditions in the leases of the land and partly because almost all the warehouses were built for the corn trade.

All the warehouses have brick walls and slate roofs, and the many small windows usually have stone lintels and cills. The window openings were as much for ventilation as for light and they were originally fitted with wooden shutters rather than glass. Many window openings had bars to meet the security requirements for bonded stores, where foreign goods could be stored without paying import duty. The interior walls were usually coated with whitewash to minimise the need for internal illumination. The Canal Company was very concerned about the fire risk and naked flames were prohibited. Some of the warehouses have a few slightly larger windows on the ground floor, which were for illuminating an office, and some even had a fireplace and chimney so that the office could be heated.

To carry the heavy sacks of corn, the floors rest on massive wooden beams, which usually span the whole width of the building and are supported by hollow cast-iron columns. In most of the later warehouses, the columns carry the names of the local iron-founders who made them. To avoid the beams being crushed locally by loads from the columns above, solid cast-iron pins pass through holes in the beams and transmit the vertical loads directly to the columns below. In the roof space, there were manually-operated winches used for hoisting the sacks up to the required floor. These had a large wheel with a brake that was operated by a rope hanging down outside the building and controlled by a man standing inside the loading door being used.

Although the warehouses are very similar, some evolution in design can be observed. The early warehouses (now mostly demolished) were around sixty feet long, parallel with

SOUTH WEST ELEVATION.

the dock and thirty feet wide, with a basement and three or four storeys. The lowest floor was a few feet above the ground, at a level suitable for loading to or from horse-drawn carts. The later warehouses are around one hundred feet long and forty feet wide, with an extra storey. The lowest floor was at around ground level and there was a gable end facing the dock, so that the building made better use of the land space behind the quay. Such warehouses could contain about 10,000 quarters of wheat weighing about 2,250 tons. The buildings were set back from the water to allow general access to the quays, which remained the property of the Canal Company.

Most of the early warehouses were erected for individual merchants who wanted to use the finished buildings for their own trade. Later it became common for financiers to arrange construction and then rent the building to a merchant. The lease for the land was usually for a period of sixty three years, after which the building became the property of the Canal Company. Construction work was carried out by local builders and seems to have usually taken six months to a year. Several of the warehouses are still known by the name of their original owner, but where one owner had several warehouses, other distinguishing names have come into common usage. By the end of the 19th century it had become common for the name to be painted in large letters on the outside of each warehouse.

The interior of Llanthony Warehouse, showing the array of cast-iron columns.

Warehouses on the east side of the Main Basin viewed from the lock, c.1910. In the early days, the occupiers were usually merchants who owned the corn in store but in later years it was more usual for the occupiers to be warehousemen who rented space to merchants. When the demand for storing corn declined in the 20th century, floors were let to non-waterway related businesses, particularly builders merchants but multi-storey buildings are not really suitable for modern storage practices and many were left empty. Now, it is recognised that the surviving warehouses form a unique group of Victorian dockside buildings and all are protected by Listed Building legislation.
NEIL PARKHOUSE

Foster Bros advertisement, from a c.1920 guide book to Gloucester.

J. Reynolds & Co. advertisement, from a c.1920 guide to the Gloucester & Sharpness Canal.

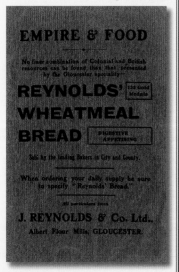

Main Docks Buildings

KEY TO MAP

1. **North Warehouse** (1826-27), a semi-detached pair financed by the Canal Co.
2. **Lock Warehouse** (1834), one of several built for corn merchants J. & C. Sturge. The present name is of recent origin.
3. Site of the **West Quay Warehouses** (1830-34), a row of nine warehouses built for various merchants (including corn merchants J. & C. Sturge) demolished in the 1960s.
4. **Engine House** (from 1834) for pumping water from the River Severn.
5. **Alexandra Warehouse** (1870), built for corn merchants J.E. & S.H. Fox.
6. **Fox's Malthouse** (1888), built for corn merchants J.E. & S.H. Fox.
7. **Great Western Warehouse** (1863), one of four financed by merchant William Partridge. It was reduced to a single storey after a fire in 1945.
8. **Foster Brothers Oil & Cake Mills** (1862 & 1891-93). In the second half of the 20th century, the buildings were used by West Midlands Farmers and known as **Provender Mill**.
9. **Midland Railway Transit Shed** (1867) at the former High Orchard goods yard.
10. **Downing's Malthouses** (1876, 1895 & 1901), built for maltsters G. & W.E. Downing.
11. **Pillar Warehouse** (1838), a semi-detached pair financed by merchants Samuel Baker and J.M. Shipton. Baker's half was later bought by corn merchant W.C. Lucy, and the whole building is now known as **Pillar & Lucy House**.
12. **Llanthony Warehouse** (1873), built for corn merchants Wait & James.
13. **Albion Cottages** (c.1820), purchased by the Canal Co. in 1847.
14. **Weighbridge House** (1849).
15. **Biddle Warehouse** (1830), financed by Stroud miller John Biddle.
16. **Shipton Warehouse** (1833), financed by merchant J.M. Shipton.
17. **Mariners Chapel** (1849).
18. **Reynolds Warehouse** (1840), one of several built for corn merchants J. & C. Sturge. The Reynolds name came into use after the building was leased by J. Reynolds & Co. of the Albert Mills in 1927.
19. **Vinings Warehouse** (1840), built for corn merchant C.J. Vining.
20. **Albert Warehouse** (1851), one of four financed by merchant William Partridge and converted to the **Albert Flour Mills** in 1869.
21. **Britannia Warehouse** (1861), one of four financed by merchant William Partridge. It was completely rebuilt in 1989 after a fire.
22. **Phillpotts Warehouse** (1846), built for corn merchant A.H. Phillpotts.
23. **Kimberley Warehouse** (1846), financed by Humphrey Brown and initially leased to corn merchant J.P. Kimberley.
24. **Herbert Warehouse** (1846), financed by solicitor Samuel Herbert.
25. **Victoria Warehouse** (1849), one of four financed by merchant William Partridge.
26. **Offices** for merchants (1848).
27. **Custom House** (1845).
28. **City Flour Mills** (1850 & c1854), built for the brothers J. & J. Hadley. The mill was later owned and managed by Priday Metford & Co. and the buildings are now known as **Pridays Mill**.
29. **Dock Office** (from 1831).

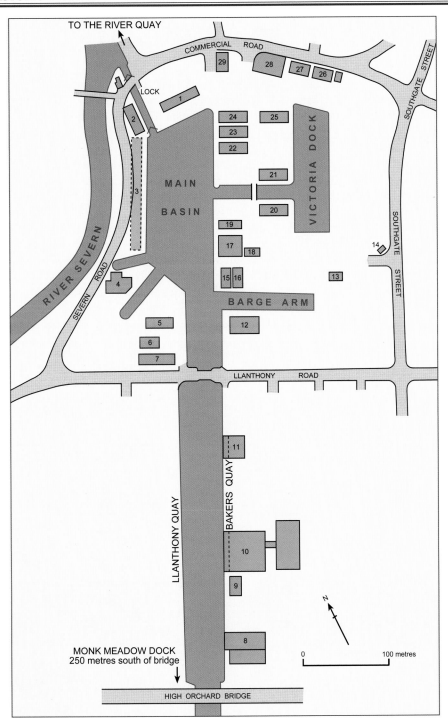

TO THE RIVER QUAY

COMMERCIAL ROAD

LOCK

RIVER SEVERN

SEVERN ROAD

MAIN

BASIN

SOUTHGATE STREET

VICTORIA DOCK

SOUTHGATE STREET

BARGE ARM

LLANTHONY ROAD

LLANTHONY QUAY

BAKERS QUAY

MONK MEADOW DOCK
250 metres south of bridge

0   100 metres

N

HIGH ORCHARD BRIDGE

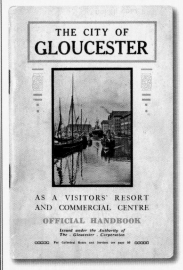

The cover of a c.1925 guide to Gloucester.

John Harker advertisement from a c.1950 guide to Gloucester. The illustration shows a barge passing through Sharpness.

Main Basin

The Main Basin is the terminus of the ship canal from Sharpness and it was where sea-going ships discharged their cargoes, either into the warehouses or direct into narrow canal boats to be taken on to destinations in the Midlands. The basin was constructed between 1794 and 1799, by gangs of men working only with spades and wheelbarrows. The barrows were wheeled over lines of planks and the earth was tipped out to build up the surrounding land, particularly the bank by the river. The basin was dug to a depth of eighteen feet, which must have been a challenging undertaking for its time, and it is not surprising that five successive contractors were employed before the work was completed.

After the canal was opened in 1827, the basin became increasingly busy with ships from mainland Europe and North America, and some had to moor in the middle while waiting for a spare berth. In February 1832, Telford noted thirty-three sea-going vessels in the basin. During the 19th century, sailing vessels predominated and their magnificent masts often towered above the warehouses. An observer in 1860 reported that the basin was so crowded that ships became hemmed in by a labyrinth of other craft and their ropes. There was a continuous babel of strange voices, as orders were shouted between deck, hold and mast-head, and there were sounds of ropes creaking and pulley blocks screeching as heavy sacks of grain or baulks of timber were lifted ashore. The visiting seamen included Frenchmen from the rich vine districts of Brittany, Italians from the fertile plantations around Palermo, negroes escaped from the slave states of America and a sprinkling of Norwegians, Danes, Dutchmen and Germans.

A barquentine on tow up the canal to Gloucester, c. 1920.

The Main Basin from the North Quay. A painting by Harley Crossley, based on a photograph taken in 1883. The ship on the right is moored to a buoy in the middle of the basin, and some cargo has been transferred to a canal boat alongside. On the left, several loaded canal boats have assembled ready to pass through the lock and join a tow up the River Severn.

Vessel movements were halted in February 1855 when the basin was frozen over for two weeks. During this period, a sheep roast was organised on the ice, using two ship's stoves mounted on some thick planks. Over 3,000 people gathered to watch and the ice became so crowded that the water began to lap up over it, forcing the organisers to move the roasting sheep hurriedly to a nearby timber yard. Many hundreds of people had a taste of the meat, although it was not fully cooked through.

A celebrity visitor in August 1899 was Capt. Howard Blackburn, who sailed single handed from Gloucester, Massachusetts in a thirty foot cutter. His achievement was the more remarkable as he had previously lost all his fingers through frost-bite and his feet were also affected. He was welcomed at the quayside by an enthusiastic crowd of sightseers who had to be restrained by the police and he was taken in an open carriage to the Guildhall for a civic reception.

In the 20th century, the number of big sailing ships declined, while steamers and motor vessels became more common, although some small sailing craft continued to trade to Gloucester for many years. The basin was also used by barges on their way between Avonmouth and the Midlands, and by narrow canal boats that traded between Gloucester and the Birmingham area.

ABOVE: Capt. Howard Blackburn on his boat GREAT WESTERN, *in which he sailed single handed from Gloucester, Massachusetts in 1899.*
NEIL PARKHOUSE

LEFT: The steam coaster STOCK FORCE *of Whitehaven simultaneously discharging to Biddle Warehouse and to the barge* AVON *alongside c.1910.*
NEIL PARKHOUSE

North Warehouse

The Main Basin with the North Warehouse prominent in the left background, c.1910. On the right, coastal sailing vessels mingle with the canal boats and barges of the Severn & Canal Carrying Co., based on the corner of the Barge Arm. This side of the docks was served by the rails of the Midland Railway Co., as evidenced by the number of their wagons in view.
NEIL PARKHOUSE

The North Warehouse at the head of the Main Basin is of particular importance, as it was the first to be built and it served as a model for all those that followed. It was built by the Gloucester & Berkeley Canal Company and was completed just in time for the opening of the canal in 1827. Its siting was recommended by Thomas Telford, who was supervising the completion of the canal, and the detailed design was provided by Bartin Haigh, a Liverpool builder who had probably had experience of constructing dock warehouses in his home town. A stone tablet near the top of the front wall records that the builders were W. Rees & Son.

The building was designed so that individual floors on each side of the central partition wall could be rented to different merchants. There were two sets of boxed-in stairs with lockable doors on all floors, so that each merchant only had access to his own goods and to the shared hoisting winches that were installed in the roof space over the loading doors. The early tenants for the main floors were mostly local merchants, who started importing wheat, barley and oats from Ireland and from Europe, whilst the brick-vaulted cellars were used for storing wines and spirits imported from Portugal and France. Later, floors were rented by larger merchants who had their own warehouses but still used part of the Canal Company's building for additional space when required. In due course, this multiple occupation died out and it was usual for one merchant to rent all the floors in one half of the building.

Around The North Quay

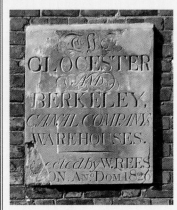

O n the corner of the North Warehouse is a former ship's bell, which used to be rung by a watchman to signal the dockers' starting and finishing times. It also served occasionally as an alarm bell, if there was a fire on board a ship or in a warehouse. In the 1940s, the bell was transferred to a light tower at Shepperdine on the Severn estuary, to be a navigation aid during foggy weather. It was re-erected on the warehouse by the Rotary Club of Gloucester and the Gloucester Civic Trust to mark the successful restoration of the warehouse.

On the quay in front of the warehouse are remnants of the former dock railway system and a restored steam crane, similar to that used by the Dock Company for discharging ships. Near to the quay edge are some large stones that once formed the foundations of a manually-operated crane.

ABOVE: The builder's plaque on the North Warehouse.

To the east of the North Warehouse is the former office of the Gloucester & Berkeley Canal Company, the organisation responsible for operating the canal and for developing the dock estate. The building also included living accommodation for the Company's clerk. When the company was nationalised in 1948, the building became the local office of what became British Waterways. A plaque on the wall commemorates the visit of the Duke of Gloucester to a boat festival in 1980, which celebrated the 400th anniversary of the port of Gloucester charter and also drew attention to the leisure potential of the docks.

BELOW: Children posing on the North Quay c.1887. Behind them, a guyed pole and tackle were being used to transfer sacks from a barge to the wagon.
GLOUCESTERSHIRE ARCHIVES

Opposite the former office today is a reconstructed doorway which formerly led into the Docks Coffee House. This was established in 1877 by the chaplain of the Mariners Chapel to provide the dock workers with a cheap alternative to beer. Sandwiches and cocoa were provided as well as coffee, and at times the building was frequented by about three hundred men a day. The chaplain also organised a rowing boat to take refreshment round to ships in the docks and to men working in the timber yards down the canal. The nearby drinking fountain was provided by the Local Board of Health in 1863 as previously there had been no public supply in the docks. It was originally intended for the dock workers, but it was sometimes monopolised by seamen filling water casks for their ships.

East Quay Warehouses

Top Below: MV Steady in front of Herbert, Kimberley and Phillpotts warehouses in October 1965.
Bottom: Barque Gers of London in front of Vinings, Reynolds and Biddle warehouses in September 1900. The vessel alongside is a steam winch to help discharge the cargo.
Gloucestershire Archives

Herbert, Kimberley and Phillpotts warehouses, at the northern end of the East Quay, were built in 1846 when a large increase in foreign imports was expected due to the repeal of the Corn Laws which abolished the duties on foreign corn. Phillpotts Warehouse was the first to be completed and the owner arranged for about 70 of the builder's men to be *'bountifully entertained at a supper'* at a local tavern, to celebrate the custom of house-rearing. These warehouses were huge buildings for their time and their construction must have stretched the contemporary technology

to the limit. While a wooden beam weighing 1.5 tons was being lifted into the top of an adjoining warehouse, it slipped and struck one end of a plank on which a man was standing. The unfortunate man was thrown six feet into the air, before falling 50 or 60 feet to the ground where he died instantly. Three weeks later, 7,000 slates were being accumulated at high level prior to being laid on the roof of the same warehouse. The load proved too much for the beam on which they were temporarily stored, and the slates and two workers plunged to the ground. Amazingly, the workers survived with only moderate injuries but nearly all the slates were smashed to pieces.

Vinings Warehouse on the East Quay is unusual, as it originally had a double-height ground floor which was occupied for nine

years by a firm of iron merchants. Later, an intermediate floor was inserted, supported by additional columns. The adjoining Reynolds Warehouse is double the normal size and the main cross beams supporting the floors had to be formed in two parts, linked end-to-end by scarf joints. Biddle Warehouse, at the southern end of the East Quay, has relatively large windows with segmental heads. The architect came from Stroud and it seems that he followed the practice used on many of the cloth mills of that area. The building originally had a hipped roof, as can be seen in the illustration on page 32, but this was later changed to have gables.

Southern Warehouses

On the south side of the Barge Arm, Llanthony Warehouse is the largest and the last of the big warehouses to be built at Gloucester. It is named after Llanthony Priory, of which there are some remains to the west of the canal. The upper floors rest on massive beams of pitch pine, which are supported on 33 cast-iron columns per floor, and the ground floor was originally laid with asphalt. Construction work took about eight months in 1873 and cost a little over £7,000, and when it was completed the owners entertained the workmen to 'a very substantial meat tea'. The warehouse was threatened with demolition in 1971, when the quay wall in front of it moved forward and subsided into the basin. However, the wall was eventually re-constructed without any adverse effects on the warehouse foundations. The building was later thoroughly renovated to house the National Waterways Museum, opened in 1988.

The quay to the south of Llanthony Warehouse was for many years the berth of the fire-float SALAMANDER. Built in 1906 by Abdela & Mitchell at Brimscombe, the boat had steam powered pumps which could deliver one thousand gallons per minute through six hoses and could also operate underwater jets to provide propulsion. In its first year of operation, it was called out to three fires on successive nights in timber yards down the canal. A young lad admitted starting the fires, saying he wanted to see the fire-float in action.

On the opposite side of the dock, the Great Western Warehouse was another large building, which was named after its size and location – not after the renowned railway company of the same name. As well as being used for storing grain, it later housed sugar for some years and so when a fire broke out in 1945, it quickly spread throughout the building and flames were seen leaping upwards to a height of 150 feet. The fire-float SALAMANDER was brought across from her berth but initially she was not tied up properly and when the main water jet was turned on, the whole boat swung round and the jet soaked spectators who had gathered on Llanthony Bridge. The fire was eventually brought under control but the damage to the building was so bad that most of the structure had to be demolished and the ground floor was converted into a single storey warehouse.

A test turnout for the crew of the fire-float SALAMANDER in front of Llanthony Warehouse in the early 1930s. The test was arranged following concern about the effectiveness of the fire-float, due to the time it took to raise steam. When the signal was given, the crew ran from the fire station and had the pumps working in less than ten minutes. This was considered so successful that there was no further talk of getting rid of the vessel for many years.
THE WATERWAYS TRUST

Western Warehouses

The Alexandra Warehouse, near the dry docks, originally had a small engine house at the west end to provide power for elevators and for a small mill. Unfortunately, in 1875, a spark from the mill chimney started a fire in the wooden eaves of the warehouse and the local firemen could do nothing about it, as their manually-pumped jets could not reach the upper floors. The firemen just had to stand by, as one floor after another gave way and burning corn poured out of the many windows, forming great mounds around the building. In the excitement, two children fell into the canal and had to be rescued. After five hours, the fire had come down to the third storey, which the water jets could reach and the fire was gradually brought under control. When the warehouse was rebuilt, the overhanging eaves where the fire had started were eliminated and the walls were extended upwards to form parapets instead.

On the West Quay of the Main Basin, there was formerly a row of early warehouses running the full length of the quay, and for many years the southernmost building was used as the St. Owen's Flour Mills. The warehouse at the north end of the row was built on pillars to provide a covered wharf underneath but this was demolished after it was gutted by fire in 1917. The condition of the other warehouses deteriorated and they were all demolished in the 1960s.

The warehouse by the lock is in a surprising location, as it does not have convenient access to a ship discharging in the Main Basin but this disadvantage was evidently accepted because there was a lack of any better site available at the time. The warehouse originally had rather widely spaced cast-iron columns supporting the floors, and it was later found necessary to add intermediate columns and beams to provide extra support. At the same time, the lowest floor was made level with the ground instead of it originally being three feet above. The new columns carry their maker's name, whilst the new beams are in two overlapping halves which are bolted together. The warehouse had some large windows inserted in the 1920s, when the building was used by Gopsill Brown & Sons for cleaning and repairing sacks which were hired by farmers and by merchants handling imported grain.

Docks From The Air

An aerial view of Gloucester Docks from the north-east in 1928, with the big warehouses clustered around the Main Basin (right) and the Victoria Dock (left). In the distance, can be seen the canal to Sharpness (upper left) and the Llanthony goods yard of the Great Western Railway (upper right). Beside the Victoria Dock in the foreground is the grain suction plant, with its overhead conveyor to the City Flour Mills. ENGLISH HERITAGE NMR/AEROFILMS

Gloucester Lock

Gloucester Lock is the means by which cargo barges and narrow canal boats accessed the River Severn on their way to the Midlands. Originally the lock had two chambers and the recesses for the middle gates can still be seen. In the event of a river flood, special stop gates at the river end can be closed to stop excess water flooding into the docks. The lock was brought into operation in 1812, to allow some use of the basin before the ship canal was completed. On the opening day, as a barge laden with coal was passing through, some young men let off three swivel guns to celebrate the event. Wishing to cause a louder report than usual, the charge of one of them had been rammed down very forcibly with wet wadding and when the match was applied, the gun exploded, wounding a bystander and the youth who fired the shot so badly that they both died.

ABOVE: Gloucester Lock viewed from the bank of the River Severn c.1850.

BELOW: The 375-ton capacity tanker barge WESTERNDALE H entering Gloucester Lock c.1955.

Once the ship canal was completed and seagoing ships were bringing cargoes to Gloucester, traffic through the lock increased, as an ever growing number of narrow canal boats carried corn, timber and other cargoes up the river to Worcester or Stourport and then through the narrow canals to Birmingham and the Black Country. The coming of the railways brought competition for carrying goods to the Midlands and the lock was deepened in 1892 to allow the use of larger vessels which were more economic. The barge traffic continued to flourish into the 1960s but then declined rapidly.

The house beside the lock was the home of the lock keeper, who was responsible for collecting tolls on boats passing through and he had an office at the north end. Before being appointed, because he would be handling money, he had to arrange a surety who would pay up if he ever defaulted. For each vessel which passed, the lock keeper recorded the name and cargo in a ledger and collected the appropriate toll. For regular carriers having an account with the Company, he only had to record the traffic and the account was settled monthly. For opening and closing the gates, the lock keeper was assisted by lock men, until hydraulic equipment was installed in the 1960s.

Riverside Quay

Before the docks were built, waterborne cargoes were loaded and unloaded at the riverside Quay, towards the far end of the reach visible from Gloucester Lock. The Quay was mainly used by barges bringing coal from Shropshire or general merchandise from up-river towns or from Bristol but occasional arrivals of sea-going ships are also recorded. The river at that time was tidal and so vessels had to moor in the centre of the channel to remain afloat at low water or they could just settle on the shelving bank. Behind the Quay were many small warehouses and yards for storing the cargoes being transhipped, and there were several public houses frequented by the bargemen. The only building surviving from those days is the early 18th century stone-faced Custom House, which had a store-room on the ground floor and offices above.

BELOW: Barges in the tidal river off Gloucester Quay by John Edmund Niemann (1858). GLOUCESTER MUSEUMS

BOTTOM: River tug SEVERN ACTIVE off Gloucester Quay c.1960.

In the early days of the docks, the unimproved state of the river meant that heavily laden barges could not use the lock when the tide was low. This was not remedied until the 1870s, when a weir was constructed downstream at Llanthony to ensure a minimum depth of water in the river. A few years later, the present stone quay wall was constructed, projecting more into the river and as it was so high, it formerly had several sets of steps set into the wall to give access to the boats moored there. Traffic on the river was severely affected by competition from the railways but the Quay continued to be used for receiving coal until well into the 20th century.

The normal summer level of the river is about 3.8 metres below the water in the docks but after periods of heavy rain the river can rise above the dock level. During a famous flood in 1852, it so happened that the stop gates had been removed for overhaul and it took frantic efforts by the maintenance team to prop the ordinary gates against the pressure of the river. A higher flood in 1947 almost lapped over the stonework of the lock and there was much concern again in 2007 when it was thought this level would be exceeded but fortunately the floods receded before that happened.

Dry Docks

BELOW: A timber lighter being repaired in the large dry dock in 1936.

BOTTOM: Steam tug SPEEDWELL in the small dry dock, also in 1936.

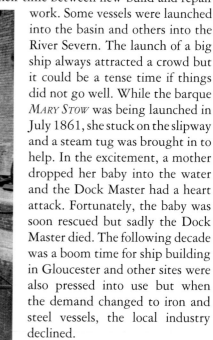

The old wooden sailing ships were often in need of maintenance and so it was important to have adequate dry dock facilities where work could be done on a vessel's hull. The small dry dock was enlarged to its present size in 1837. A culvert was provided to allow water from the dock to be drained out into the river but if the river level was high, it used to take eight men seven hours to pump the water out. A stone in the north wall of the dock was inscribed 'CG 6 Ft' in 1845 to mark that the boundary of the city of Gloucester at that time changed direction six feet in front of the stone. The large dry dock was built in 1853 to accommodate the bigger vessels that were then using the canal. As the work was nearing completion, the landlord of the nearby Black Swan was given permission to hold a party in the dock but there is no record of whether such an extraordinary event ever took place. For this dock, a steam engine was provided to pump the water out when necessary. In the 20th century, the two dry docks were much used for overhauling the many local barges, tugs and canal maintenance craft that were in use on the canal.

The area to the south of the dry docks was formerly the site of a ship-building yard, where many wooden sailing ships were built by craftsmen who shared their time between new-build and repair work. Some vessels were launched into the basin and others into the River Severn. The launch of a big ship always attracted a crowd but it could be a tense time if things did not go well. While the barque *MARY STOW* was being launched in July 1861, she stuck on the slipway and a steam tug was brought in to help. In the excitement, a mother dropped her baby into the water and the Dock Master had a heart attack. Fortunately, the baby was soon rescued but sadly the Dock Master died. The following decade was a boom time for ship building in Gloucester and other sites were also pressed into use but when the demand changed to iron and steel vessels, the local industry declined.

Engine House

The Engine House between the two dry docks was built in 1834, for a beam engine that pumped water from the River Severn to make up that lost through operation of the locks. Provision had been made to take supplies from streams that flowed into the canal but these were not enough to maintain the proper water level in dry weather. In later years, the machinery was updated and the building was much modified to suit. The old steam engines have long since been removed but the stump of the chimney remains as a reminder of the building's former use. Regular pumping is still required because, as well as the losses through use of the locks, water is also taken from the canal at Purton to provide drinking water for Bristol. The present pumps are electric-powered, under the open part of the West Quay, and a former pump has been preserved nearby.

The water pumped from the River Severn contains a high proportion of silt which tends to settle out in the Main Basin. This can be particularly bad during the summer months and it was usually necessary to dredge the whole basin during the autumn to re-establish a depth of about 16 feet. The steam-powered bucket dredger formerly used for this task later became a working exhibit at the National Waterways Museum. In recent years, instead of dredging, a powerful floating pump has been used to stir up the silt into suspension and by leaving the sluices open at the lock, much of the silt is carried out into the river.

The building adjoining the engine house dates from the 1890s, when the Dock Company provided new workshops for their maintenance craftsmen, who had previously been based at Saul Lodge near the mid-point of the canal. If one of the repair yard workers fell into the water by accident, it was the tradition that he could go home for the rest of the day and he was known as the Mayor of Gloucester for that day. One shipwright who was mad on cricket heard that the county team was batting well, so he pushed his apprentice into the dock and jumped in to rescue him, making a lot of fuss to be sure they were seen. The foreman heard the fuss and told the shipwright to take the boy home. Then they both went and watched the cricket all afternoon – wringing wet!

The bell of the ship ATLAS on the corner of the North Warehouse.

BELOW LEFT: British Waterways tugs SPEEDWELL and FREIGHT MOVER in the large dry dock, with the engine house and a modern extension to the workshops behind, c.1990.

BELOW: The Dock Company's steam bucket dredger at work in the Main Basin in the 1950s.
THE WATERWAYS TRUST

BELOW: Schooner DISPATCH in the Victoria Dock waiting to load salt for a port in Ireland c.1932.
GRAHAM FARR COLLECTION

BOTTOM: The ceremonial launching of the lifeboat GLOUCESTER at the head of the Victoria Dock in 1867.
GLOUCESTERSHIRE ARCHIVES

Victoria Dock

The Victoria Dock was opened in 1849, to accommodate the growth in imports following the repeal of the Corn Laws. It required a major excavation, cutting into the sloping ground, and much of the spoil was taken to Over Bridge for the railway embankment that was being formed there. This led to complaints that the carts being used were dropping soil in the streets of the town and the drivers were warned by the magistrates against overloading and *'furious driving'*. The dock was formally opened on 18th April 1849, when thousands of spectators watched as ten vessels entered it with their flags flying and crews manning the yards. A 10-ton manually operated crane was installed at the south end of the dock, the post of which is still *in situ*. The entrance cut from the Main Basin was originally crossed only by a footbridge and the present Victoria Bridge is a later installation built to improve the railway system in the docks. The dock was also known as the Salt Basin, as this was where salt brought by rail from Droitwich and Stoke Prior was transferred to sea-going ships for Ireland and mainland Europe. Small schooners collected salt here until the 1940s.

A special event took place here in April 1867, when a new lifeboat was officially launched and handed over to the National Lifeboat Institution. The money for the boat had been raised locally and it was to be named *GLOUCESTER*. Only ticket holders were supposed to enter the docks area but the gates were forced open and a crowd of over 8,000 swarmed in round the Victoria Dock. After a few formal speeches, the boat was launched with the crew on board, thereby creating an enormous sheet of spray. It was rowed round the dock, rescuing volunteers who had thrown themselves into the water and it was then capsized by a crane to demonstrate its self-righting ability. Afterwards, the streets remained crowded and the resources of the inns and refreshment shops were said to have been seriously taxed.

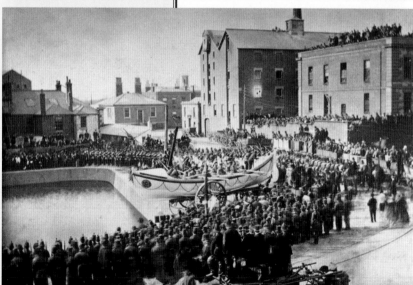

Pridays Mill

The large buildings to the north-west of the dock housed what was originally called the City Flour Mills, built for the Hadley brothers in the 1850s. This is an early example of the gradual movement of the industry from water-powered sites in the country to steam-powered mills at the ports. The original plant in the eastern building consisted of a few pairs of grindstones and some flour dressing machines driven by a steam engine. The venture was so successful that it was soon necessary to build an adjoining warehouse to the west, and two new steam engines and other machinery were installed to double the output of the mill. Unfortunately, the crankshaft of one of the steam engines fractured and needed to be sent back to the manufacturers at Greenwich to serve as a pattern for a new one. This led to a landmark court case which is commemorated by a plaque on the building.

From 1886, the mill was run by Priday Metford & Co. Soon after they took over, the warehouse was badly damaged by a spectacular fire which burned for two hours. Floors collapsed and a strong southerly wind almost blew the flames across Commercial Road but fortunately the mill itself was not seriously affected and they were soon back in business. For many years, wheat delivered in bulk by barge from Sharpness needed to be put into sacks to be taken 50 yards to the mill. Then in the 1920s, this labour intensive operation was superseded by a suction plant, with an overhead conveyor to the mill. In the 1970s, the delivery of wheat changed over to road transport and this continued until the mill closed in 1994.

To the east of Pridays Mill is the former Custom House, built in 1845 to a design by Sidney Smirke, with a stone frontage facing Commercial Road. This was the base for customs officers who checked and recorded the arrival of foreign cargoes, who monitored the movement of goods in and out of bonded stores, and who collected the appropriate duties. Clerks also kept a register of all the ships belonging to the port, and they checked on the seamen's terms and conditions of employment.

The City Flour Mills, c.1900. The crankshaft of a steam engine in the central building fractured in 1853 and when it was delayed in transit back to the manufacturers, the Hadley brothers sued the carrier for their loss of profits. This led to a landmark ruling that any damages for breach of contract should take account of what might reasonably have been contemplated by both parties at the time that the contract was made. The case, referred to as Hadley v Baxendale, is known to lawyers all over the world and is still studied and discussed today.
GLOUCESTERSHIRE ARCHIVES

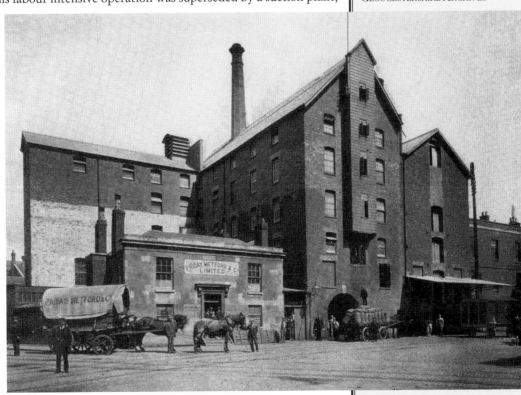

Around the Victoria Dock

To the east of the Custom House is a large building that provided office accommodation for a number of local merchants, with storage vaults at the dock level. Further east is a smaller building that for many years was occupied by a ship chandler, who had his business premises at dock level and his accommodation above.

The three warehouses on the west side of the Victoria Dock, named Victoria, Britannia and Albert, were all financed by iron merchant and carrier William Partridge, who leased the buildings to various corn merchants. In between Victoria and Britannia warehouses were two long corn sheds and other assorted buildings. Albert Warehouse was converted to a flour mill in 1869, a boiler house was built to the south and other buildings were added later. In 1880, the mill was the first in the district to have roller milling machines installed and the manager became famous for the evening classes he organised for others to learn the new techniques. As the business expanded, the company used the nearby Vinings and Reynolds warehouses for storing wheat and flour, and there was an overhead conveyor between Vinings Warehouse and the mill. A remnant of a siding serving the mill can be seen adjoining Victoria Bridge. The mill continued operating until 1977, when the equipment was stripped out and the ancillary buildings demolished.

On the east side of the dock stood a single-storey iron transit shed, which was intended for the temporary storage of malting barley while waiting to be sent on via the Midland Railway. In the event, however, it was mainly used for storing general cargoes, cement and some salt.

A small building outside the Southgate Street entrance, echoing the style of the bridge-keepers' houses along the canal, once housed the mechanism of a weighbridge. Wagons were weighed empty and loaded, and the operator issued a ticket showing the weight that had been delivered or collected. It was still in use in the 1960s, particularly for weighing builders' materials, and on one occasion it weighed an elephant as a publicity stunt for a visiting circus!

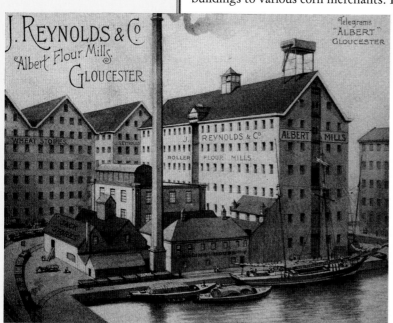

ABOVE: A Reynolds & Co's Albert Flour Mills advertisement c.1900. GLOUCESTERSHIRE ARCHIVES

RIGHT: Sailing vessels moored in the Victoria Dock c.1894. NEIL PARKHOUSE

Mariners Chapel

In the early days of the docks, visiting sailors were encouraged to attend one of the local parish churches on Sundays but they were reluctant to do so, saying they did not have any smart clothes to wear. The idea therefore arose of building a special chapel in the docks, where sailors working clothes would not look out of place. Money was donated by the merchants and other public spirited citizens, a building was erected, and a special chaplain was appointed by the bishop to minister to the seamen and the dockland community. The opening service was held on the 11th February 1849 and subsequent services were well attended, particularly on Sunday evenings. Unfortunately, it was found initially that a fair number of people from the city were also joining in and they had to be encouraged to return to their own churches for fear that their presence would deter the seamen.

ABOVE: The chaplain of the Mariners Chapel preparing for an open-air service c.1915.
THE WATERWAYS TRUST

The chaplain made a point of visiting each ship when it arrived and he often called at the sailors' home in the town to spread the word of God. He sold bibles, distributed tracts in many different languages and encouraged the men to give up drink and gambling, and to come to the chapel. Some special services in foreign languages were arranged occasionally. For those who were still unwilling to come into the chapel, the chaplain sometimes took out a portable organ and held a service by the dockside or on board a ship. It was often frustrating work, as few of the sailors stayed in port for long but it was apparently appreciated by many.

BELOW: The Mariners Chapel in the 1880s.
GLOUCESTERSHIRE ARCHIVES

The nucleus of his congregation was drawn from the dock labourers and their families, and for them he organised bible classes and an adult evening school. A highlight of the year was the annual tea party, which was held in one of the warehouses and was attended by several hundred people. Later, a Mariners Hall and Reading Room were established in a former cheese warehouse on the corner of Southgate Street and Llanthony Road.

The chapel is still in use and visitors are welcome. The old stained glass windows came from the former St. Catharine's Church in Gloucester, when this was demolished in 1921. Modern windows mark the 150th anniversary of the opening of the chapel and the 200th anniversary of laying the first stone in the docks.

Tramroad

The first rail system to link with the docks was a tramroad between Gloucester and Cheltenham, opened in 1811. This had flanged cast-iron rails, laid on stone sleeper blocks at a gauge of three feet six inches and the wagons were drawn by horses. The main aim was to supply Cheltenham with coal and roadstone. Although the canal was far from complete at this time, the advent of the tramroad prompted the Canal Company to bring the lock and basin into use to provide a safe place off the tidal river for transferring goods to the tramroad wagons. The route of the tramroad left the dock estate on the south side of the access road to Southgate Street and a gateway was provided here when the dock estate was later enclosed by a wall. The line of the tramroad through this gateway has been marked in the paving and ten recovered sleeper blocks have been placed in position to carry some cast-iron rails and two replica wagons.

In 1840, a main line railway was opened between Gloucester and Cheltenham as part of the line to Birmingham but initially there was no connection to the docks because of opposition in Parliament. The tramroad therefore took on a new role of carrying goods between the docks and Gloucester station. However, through traffic was hampered by the need to transfer goods between standard gauge and tramroad gauge wagons and so in 1844, standard gauge rails were also laid along the route of the tramroad. This additional role ended in 1848, when a branch from the main line into the docks was opened, but the tramroad continued to provide a local service until the line was closed in 1861 and the rails were taken up.

The two small houses near the Southgate Street entrance to the docks are named after the former Albion Hotel, the large stone building on the opposite side of the street. In the early days, they were occupied by local traders, including a blacksmith who presumably provided shoes for the horses pulling wagons on the tramroad. In 1848, the houses were bought by the Canal Company and used to house their employees. Over the years, occupants included two toll clerks, a lockman, three members of the engineering staff and two drivers of the steam pumping engine on the opposite side of the Main Basin.

ABOVE: Detail from the design for the seal of the Gloucester & Cheltenham Tramroad Company.

BELOW: Midland Railway Co. horses with a wagon on the North Quay, c.1887.
GLOUCESTERSHIRE ARCHIVES

Railways

After much debate and negotiation, the Midland Railway Company eventually obtained Parliamentary approval for a standard gauge branch to the docks, and a line from Gloucester station to High Orchard and the east side of the docks was opened in 1848. This line entered the dock estate immediately to the east of the Albion Cottages, continued around the north end of the Victoria Dock and along in front of the North Warehouse. Further lines branched off to serve other quays and warehouses, and these often required turntables to negotiate sharp corners around existing buildings. Six years later, the Great Western Railway opened a goods yard on Llanthony Quay. These lines were soon busy with imports being sent on to the Midlands, instead of going by boat, and with salt from Worcestershire being delivered for export, and additional tracks were laid as traffic increased. Some of the surviving lines have been reset in the modern paving.

ABOVE: British Railways 0-4-0T No. 41535 at High Orchard Wharf sidings in July 1962. Behind are Fielding & Platt's engineering works, demolished in 2008 to make way for the Gloucester Quays shopping centre. NEIL PARKHOUSE

Locomotives moved wagons to and from the main line but horses were generally employed for local movements around the dock estate, particularly if there was a need to use a turntable, which could only take one wagon at a time. The horses knew exactly where to stop to position a wagon correctly on a turntable, which was then rotated by pushing on an extending arm. For a loaded wagon, a horse could be hitched up to the arm to help get the turntable moving but care was required not to exert too much force or the wagon could swing round out of control. The horses also knew that it was worth stopping outside a warehouse where lump sugar was stored and somebody would usually give them a lump or two.

LEFT: Sister locomotive No. 41537 and wagon climbing the incline from the Victoria Dock to pass beside the Albion Cottages in 1962. In earlier times, wagons had been allowed to run back down this incline on their own, with just some braking applied. On one occasion, they came down so fast that they crashed into another wagon from which men were loading salt into a schooner. Unfortunately, the impact threw one man over the end of the wagon and the wheels passed over him, killing him instantly. BEN ASHWORTH

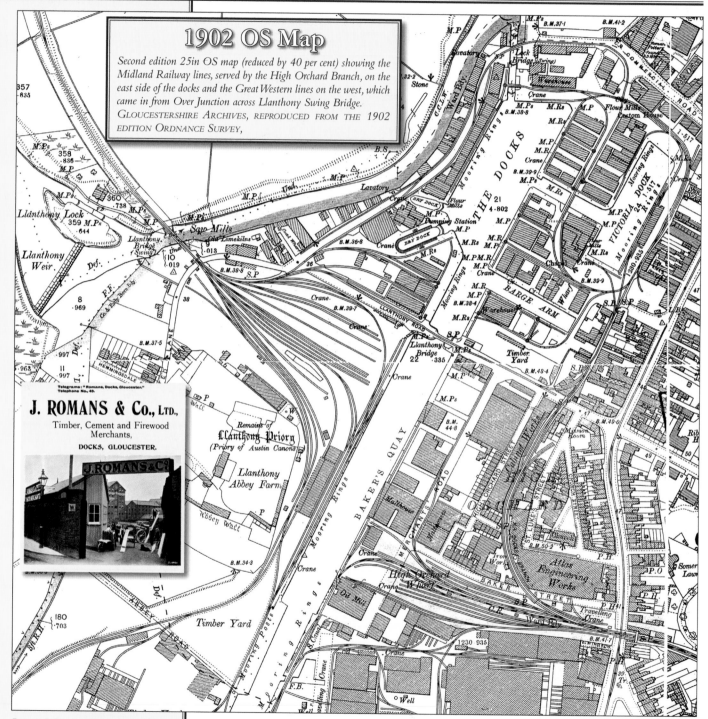

1902 OS Map

Second edition 25in OS map (reduced by 40 per cent) showing the Midland Railway lines, served by the High Orchard Branch, on the east side of the docks and the Great Western lines on the west, which came in from Over Junction across Llanthony Swing Bridge.

GLOUCESTERSHIRE ARCHIVES, REPRODUCED FROM THE 1902 EDITION ORDNANCE SURVEY.

Telegrams: "Romans, Docks, Gloucester."
Telephone No. 45.

J. ROMANS & Co., LTD.,

Timber, Cement and Firewood
Merchants,

DOCKS, GLOUCESTER.

INSET: *J. Romans & Co. advertisement, c.1920.*

The Barge Arm

The Barge Arm was constructed in 1824-25 to provide space for smaller vessels to load and unload whilst keeping the Main Basin clear for sea-going ships. The design was specified by Thomas Telford, who was supervising the later stages of building the canal. As it was only intended for barges and boats, he said the depth did not need to exceed ten feet and the height of the quay walls need only be two feet. The surrounding land was divided up into eighteen yards on each side, each yard having a frontage of only twenty feet, although some tenants rented more than one yard. Each pair of yards was served by a siding of the Gloucester & Cheltenham Tramroad. A surviving inventory of 1834 shows that one yard was surrounded by seven foot high fencing, with a pair of gates which opened on wheels. In the yard was a manually operated cast-iron crane capable of lifting seven tons, a tramroad wagon and several barrows used for transferring cargoes between the boats and the tramroad.

Several yards on the north side, near to Biddle and Shipton warehouses, were occupied by a succession of firms who carried a wide range of general cargoes for other merchants between the Bristol Channel ports and the Midlands. Barges and small steamers traded down to Bristol and the South Wales ports, and narrow canal boats traded up to Birmingham and the Black Country. This area of the Barge Arm became a busy centre for transferring cargoes between vessels or between vessel and yard. Small sheds and offices were built on some of the yards and the ground floor of Biddle Warehouse was used when needed for storing goods in transit. Two cast-iron crane posts survive as a reminder of these former activities. The other yards around the Barge Arm were occupied by traders handling coal, stone, timber and builders materials for local use, and a large single-storey corn shed was built near the north-east corner.

When the tramroad closed in 1861, arrangements were made for the Midland Railway to lay rails serving the south side of the Barge Arm in order to continue the existing stone traffic to Cheltenham. To facilitate this new line, the Canal Company raised the level of the quay wall on this side by two feet.

ABOVE: *Buchanan & Co., coal merchants, had an office between the Albion Cottages and the head of the Barge Arm, which can also be seen in the lower picture on page 29. This advertisement comes from a c.1950 guide to Gloucester.*

ABOVE: *A hand-operated crane beside the Barge Arm being used to load newsprint in 1926.*
GLOUCESTERSHIRE ARCHIVES

LEFT: *Coal being unloaded on the south side of the Barge Arm c.1905.*
GLOUCESTERSHIRE ARCHIVES

Llanthony Bridge

Llanthony Bridge is named after Llanthony Priory, of which there are some remains to the west of the canal. The present bridge is the third on the site. The original structure comprised two wooden half-spans which could be swung open to let vessels pass through. Each half-span was rotated by pushing on a long arm attached to the tail of the span, only one side needing to be opened for a small barge or boat to pass. There were no barriers to prevent access when the bridge was open – in fact it was considered a treat for children to ride on a span while it was being swung. Thus, when a frightened horse with a cart was galloping out of control towards the bridge, it was only at the last minute that he realised that the far side of the bridge had been swung open. He desperately struggled to check his speed but he was projected onwards by the weight of the cart until he fell with a terrible crash on to a barge laden with salt which was passing at the time. The horse rolled on into the water and was drowned but neither the barge nor the crew sustained any material injury. From 1852, the bridge keeper lived in the house to the east of the bridge.

The old wooden structure of Llanthony Bridge was replaced by a single-span iron swing bridge in 1862. This was part of a scheme to develop property in the south-west corner of the dock estate; the new bridge was needed so that the Midland Railway could lay a line across it and into the new property. The Great Western Railway also wished to serve this area with broad gauge track and the two companies were persuaded to lay mixed gauge lines that would suit both types of rolling stock. While the bridge was being rebuilt, a rope-operated ferry was arranged for pedestrians but its handrails and steps for boarding did not appear very secure and it was 'entirely avoided by females'.

The present bascule bridge was installed in 1972 but part of the base of the previous swing bridge can still be seen on the east side.

ABOVE: The original Llanthony Bridge as depicted in the mid 19th century by Edward Smith, with Biddle and Shipton warehouses behind.
GLOUCESTER MUSEUMS

RIGHT: The second Llanthony Bridge c.1905, with narrow canal boats and a barge in the foreground.
NEIL PARKHOUSE

South of Llanthony Bridge

LEFT: *Looking north c.1895, with several large sailing ships flanking Llanthony Bridge. The Great Western and Alexandra warehouses are on the left and the Pillar Warehouse in the right foreground.*
NEIL PARKHOUSE

BELOW: *The view south from Llanthony Bridge c.1905, with the Pillar Warehouse and Downing's Malthouses on the left and a steamer beside Llanthony Quay on the right.*
NEIL PARKHOUSE

The Docks, Gloucester. Nº 4.

Bakers Quay

Ships moored by Bakers Quay in 1885, with the Pillar Warehouse in the distance and the transit shed on the right. The narrow canal boat appears to be towing something underwater – possibly a bucket which was sometimes used to steady the last boat in a tow behind a tug.
NEIL PARKHOUSE

W hen the canal was first built, the stretch to the south of Llanthony Bridge was just 70 feet wide, like the rest of the canal. It was widened in two stages, when new quays were needed to provide more space for discharging ships. Bakers Quay on the east was constructed in the 1830s to ease overcrowding in the Main Basin. It was financed by a group of local merchants and bankers led by Samuel Baker, at a time when the Canal Company was still heavily in debt and it was part of the agreement with the Company that any warehouses would be built with their upper storeys projecting forward and supported by pillars on the quay wall. This was to allow a winch in the loft to lift goods out of a ship's hold and at the same time to leave the quay open for public use.

Soon after the quay was completed, the Pillar Warehouse was constructed as two semi-detached units, with a central dividing wall and massive 60 foot long timber beams supporting the floors. Much of the rest of the quay initially served as timber yards, where ships from the Baltic and North America discharged rough-hewn logs, sawn deals and pieces suitable for masts and barrel staves.

Near the southern end of the quay, the Midland Railway established their High Orchard goods yard in 1848, after a long delay in getting Parliamentary approval for a line to the docks. The goods yard initially had its own dock as a branch off the canal but this turned out to be of little use and it was soon filled in. A line from the goods yard continued south along the canal bank, with sidings branching off to serve industrial premises and more timber yards. Following concern about sacks of imported corn being left on the quayside while waiting to be sent on by rail, the Midland Railway built an iron-frame transit shed in 1867 and this is currently still *in situ*. On the face of the quay wall in front of the shed is the inscription 'CG', marking the boundary of the City of Gloucester in the 1840s.

Buildings on Bakers Quay

In the early days, the only building on Bakers Quay was the Pillar Warehouse but during the second half of the 19th century, the adjoining timber yards were progressively built over. Two of these buildings had their upper floors projecting forward and supported on pillars in accordance with the old agreement concerning the original construction of the quay. Near the mid-point of the quay, G. & W.E. Downing built four malthouses, the last two, with upper floors supported on pillars, being completed in 1901. At the south end of the

quay, an oil and cake mill was established by Foster Brothers in 1862, where imported linseed and cotton seed was crushed to give oil and the residue was sold for cattle food. The buildings were extended considerably in the 1890s, including a rebuilding of the projecting structure following serious subsidence of the quay wall supporting the pillars.

In the 20th century, Foster Brothers had shipments of peanuts arrive by barge and when the word got around, local lads were soon on hand to snaffle a handful or two if they could without being observed. Keen to get a larger supply, two enterprising brothers mounted a raid late one evening by paddling a bath alongside a barge, shovelling peanuts into the bath and quietly paddling back to the quay steps. Just as they were about to get their booty ashore, however, they were caught in the beam of a powerful torch and a dock policeman shouted *"Don't move!"*. Knowing the area well, the brothers managed to escape in the darkness but they never learned what happened to the bath full of peanuts.

The land behind the quay was known as High Orchard as it had once been the 'high orchard' of nearby Llanthony Priory. As trade through the docks increased, this area was developed to accommodate a wide range of industries, including saw mills, iron works and chemical works, together with housing for the workers.

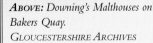

ABOVE: *Downing's Malthouses on Bakers Quay.*
GLOUCESTERSHIRE ARCHIVES

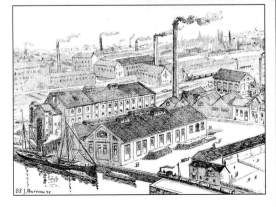

LEFT: *Foster Brothers' oil and cake mill on Bakers Quay after the extension in the early 1890s.*
GLOUCESTERSHIRE ARCHIVES

Llanthony Quay

Llanthony Quay, on the west side of the canal, was constructed by the Gloucester & Dean Forest Railway in 1852, to provide an outlet for coal from the Forest of Dean and a rail link from the South Wales line was opened two years later. To assist in handling the coal, a powerful hydraulic lift was constructed by the Great Western Railway, who had taken over operation of the line. Each railway wagon was placed on a platform which was raised by four strong chains and then the platform was tilted to let the coal tip into the hold of a waiting vessel. The process was evidently rather messy, as the local paper warned those promenading along the canal banks *that the operation will in no way add to the pleasure of their walk'*. In the event, however, walkers were not disturbed much, as many ship masters preferred to go to one of the South Wales ports to load coal.

A short length at the northern end of the quay became the base for the steam tugs which towed vessels up and down the canal. As coal exports did not flourish, the rest of the quay mainly became used for handling imports, particularly those due to be forwarded on the Great Western Railway. In the 1890s, the quay began to be used by a regular line of steamers from Antwerp and Rotterdam, operated by the Bristol Steam Navigation Company. Their main import was sugar but they also brought a wide range of other cargoes and a large transit shed with a raised floor was constructed on the quay, to hold goods waiting to go on by rail.

The railway company operated travelling steam cranes on the quayside and one driver had a nasty experience when he was transferring a new boiler from a railway wagon to a barge, on its way to Butlers Tar Works at Sandhurst. Unknown to him, the boiler was part full of water and as the load swung round, the crane tipped over into the canal, tearing up part of the railway line as it went. The cabin of the crane was smashed but the driver just managed to extricate himself and swim to safety.

The goods yard behind the quay became an important place for marshalling wagons on their way to and from South Wales, and the GWR established a sheet works there for making and servicing the tarpaulins used for covering railway wagons. The goods yard office still stands near to Llanthony Bridge.

BELOW: The Dock Company's tugs SPEEDWELL, HAZEL *and* MAYFLOWER *in 'tug corner' to the south of Llanthony Bridge c.1895.*

BOTTOM: A Bristol Steam Navigation Co. steamer alongside the GWR transit shed on Llanthony Quay, c.1905.
NEIL PARKHOUSE

South of High Orchard Bridge

High Orchard Bridge, completed in 2008, carries the last stage of Gloucester's Inner Relief Road, which provides access to the massive Gloucester Quays development. The bridge name comes from the old name of the area to the east, which was the 'high orchard' of Llanthony Priory. To the south of High Orchard Bridge, on the east side of the canal, is the site of the Gloucester Railway Carriage & Wagon Works, founded in 1860 and a major place of employment for over 100 years. On the west side of the canal, opposite the Wagon Works, is the site of a former grain silo built in the 1940s to dry and store home-grown grain.

Cutting into the canal bank on the west side of the canal is Monk Meadow Dock, which was constructed in 1892 to provide more facilities for the timber trade. In the 1920s, the dock began to be used to handle petroleum products and several oil companies erected storage tanks. A large fleet of tanker barges brought petrol and oil from Avonmouth, and some continued on up the River Severn to depots at Worcester and Stourport. A frightening incident occurred in 1958, when a tanker barge loaded with petrol was engulfed in flames and the tanker's skipper was seen hanging from its bows by his fingertips. Following a spillage, petrol had spread across the water surface and had by chance been ignited. While some men sprayed the flames with fire extinguishers, others rescued the skipper, who was taken to the Infirmary suffering from facial injuries and shock. This barge traffic died out in the 1960s, following the construction of a depot at Quedgeley served by coastal tankers.

For the next three-quarters of a mile, the east bank of the canal was lined by a series of major timber yards and saw mills. Some of these were developed during the 1840s and 1850s when huge quantities of wood were imported from the Baltic and North America for use in constructing railways, and they were still handling timber imports well into the 1970s. At times, parts of the west bank of the canal were also used for storing timber and a timber pond was formed to the south of Monk Meadow Dock in 1896, where large baulks could be left floating to avoid them drying out and cracking. Further south, Monk Meadow Quay was constructed in 1965 for use by coasters.

BELOW: Petroleum tanker barges in Monk Meadow Dock, with storage tanks beyond.
GLOUCESTERSHIRE ARCHIVES

BOTTOM: Looking north over timber yards beside the canal, with Monk Meadow timber pond in the left background.
GLOUCESTERSHIRE ARCHIVES

Handling Grain

Grain usually arrived in bulk in a ship's hold and it had to be put into sacks for transfer to a warehouse. As payment was normally by piece-work, highly efficient techniques were developed involving considerable teamwork. Each sack was filled by men using a vertical-sided metal bucket known as a bushel. When the sack was full, its contents were adjusted to the correct weight and its top was tied up with string. Then a self-tightening loop of chain on the end of a hoisting rope was thrown round its neck, so it could be lifted over the side of the ship. The man placing the loop had to be smart as, such was the fluency of the whole operation, any delay could result in him getting his hand caught and being lifted up with

The activities involved in transferring grain into a warehouse, in an illustration by Philip Moss.

the sack. For unloading a sailing ship, the hoisting rope was slung from a derrick rigged from one of the masts. For unloading a barge, a block and tackle was slung from the top of a guyed pole that was set up for the purpose.

Sacks unloaded on to the quay were lifted into a warehouse using a rope from a projecting gable and a winch worked by two men in the warehouse loft. The rope was sometimes arranged so that as one end was being used to lift a sack, the other end was descending ready for the next sack. The winch had a brake that could be operated by another rope hanging outside the building and controlled by a 'hatchman' on the floor into which the sacks were being loaded. If the sacks to be lifted were some distance in front of the warehouse, planks were leant against the warehouse wall to break the swing of the sack as it cleared the ground. In spite of this precaution, occasional accidents occurred and it was usual to lay a canvas sheet on the quayside to catch the grain from any bag that split.

Once the sack was stopped level with the appropriate floor, a man standing inside the open loading doors pushed it outwards and then let it swing back into the opening. Some sacks were received on to a sack truck and wheeled to where they were to be stored. Others were received on to a stand from which men could carry them across their backs to build up additional tiers. Use of the stand made it possible for a man to carry sacks weighing over two hundredweight (100 kg), which he would not have been able to lift from the floor.

It was hard work moving the heavy sacks about all day but the men became highly proficient in handling them and could usually put them down in just the right place to ensure the stability of the stack. One unfortunate incident occurred when a man working by the opening missed his balance. As he grabbed something to save himself from falling out, he accidentally pushed a sack truck out of the opening and it fell on a man below who died from his injuries. In later years, men working near the opening were required to wear a safety harness.

The sacks were provided by specialist firms who hired them out as required, and then ensured that they were cleaned and mended if necessary ready for re-use. To minimise the hire cost, the grain was sometimes tipped out on to the warehouse floor, although it was then usual to form a wall of full sacks around the outside to avoid too much build-up of pressure on the warehouse walls. Lack of this precaution led to a serious incident, when grain was piled too high in the single-storey corn shed beside the Barge Arm and the end wall collapsed on to the quayside, killing one worker.

ABOVE: A giant stack of some 6,000 sacks of oats delivered to Gloucester from Argentina in July 1913. The sacks, filled at the dockside, were hired from Hudson & Co.
NEIL PARKHOUSE

When the grain was taken out of store, all the loading operations were repeated in reverse order. Breaking down a high pile of sacks was done with care to avoid any risk of collapse but occasional accidents did happen, and at least one labourer was killed when some falling sacks knocked him down and crushed him. When a warehouse was being emptied, a rat hunt was usually organised and men were employed to kill the rats by kicking them or hitting them with large pieces of wood. Good ratting dogs were also welcome and great rivalry developed as to whose dog would claim the most victims.

In the 20th century, some mechanical aids were introduced to reduce the amount of labour required for handling grain. Electric winches were installed in some warehouses, whilst one warehouse had an electric-powered elevator and a helical chute for raising and lowering sacks the full height of the building. More important improvements came in the 1920s, with the use of pneumatic or Redler chain elevators and purpose-built silos that allowed grain to be handled in bulk, thus doing away with the need for filling and emptying sacks.

LEFT: A gang of corn porters with their tools. These men were photographed at Sharpness, at the other end of the canal, c.1900.

BELOW: A Redler's elevator being used to transfer grain from the barge HANNAH into Vinings Warehouse in 1934.
GRAHAM FARR COLLECTION

Handling Timber

In the early days, sailing ships delivered sawn deals and larger baulks of timber direct to the timber yards beside the canal. Men in the ship's hold prepared sling-loads of deals, which were lifted out by a derrick rigged from a mast and then men in the yard carried two or three pieces on their shoulder to the pile where that particular size of deal was being stacked. As the larger baulks were too big to be handled in this way, they were eased out of special ports in the ship's bows and allowed to drop into the water, where at busy times they obstructed passage along the canal. By the end of the 19th century, most timber arrived in big ships that needed to discharge at Sharpness, and the deals and baulks were then brought to Gloucester in lighters or as rafts.

For discharging timber from a lighter, lines of planks extending as much as a hundred yards from the quayside were set up on trestles, for the men to run along carrying the wood to pile in a highly organised operation. A carrier required considerable experience to judge the balance point correctly or otherwise he could drop the load and so waste time. Once their load was under control, they ran along the planks to where their particular size of wood was being stacked, 'flopped the handful' down on top of the pile and ran back to the boat for more. As the piles of timber grew, the access planks were raised high above the ground and the carriers needed great skill to compensate for the natural movement of the narrow swaying planks as they hurried over them.

Deals being unloaded at Joseph Griggs & Co's timber yard near Hempsted Bridge in the 1930s. Men in the lighters 'boxed up' similar sized pieces to make a 'handful' weighing up to one hundredweight. This was 'thrown up' by two men on to the shoulder of a carrier whose boast was 'What two men can lift, I can carry'. Each carrier wore a special leather pad to protect their shoulder but it was still a painful job until the skin hardened up. The load was steadied with one hand on top to hold the front end tipped down slightly, and in this way the men managed to balance and to turn great lengths of wood with apparent ease.

The construction of each pile was closely supervised to ensure that it remained stable to its full height and that there were adequate air passages to promote drying. This was carried out by a man at one end of the pile, who adjusted the position of each piece of wood delivered by the carriers. As the pile grew, he left occasional 'horns' of wood protruding so that he could lay a plank across two horns to stand on.

Speed was important to avoid delaying the ship that had brought the timber and the men were paid a piece-work rate for the amount that they moved. A gang comprised about ten to fifteen men, who usually worked hard and with great efficiency. They stopped occasionally for refreshment, which

often included a drink of beer. During the importing season, they could earn very good money but a proportion was deducted by the gang leader to pay for the beer.

When the wood was required for use, it all had to be handled again. Individual pieces were pushed over the end of the stack so that they stood upright supported by the horns protruding from the stack. Then the pieces were carried to railway wagons or narrow canal boats ready for dispatch. Speed was not so important for this operation and it was done by a gang of five or six men paid by the day.

In the 19th century, the piles could be well over 20 feet high, and it is not surprising that this led to many accidents. If a man fell from that height, it was likely that his injuries would be serious – if not fatal. Another risk was for a heavy piece of timber to fall on someone on the ground, and particularly serious was for a pile to collapse and crush someone. In the 20th century, management and workers agreed that the piles should not exceed twenty feet in height but there were still accidents. A particularly sad case was when a boy employee fell from a pile while playing hide-and-seek during his lunch break and died later in the Infirmary. As the accident did not occur during working hours, the boy's employers did not consider they were formally responsible but they did make a contribution towards his funeral expenses.

The labour-intensive procedure of running timber to pile continued throughout the first half of the 20th century and it was not until the 1960s that mechanical aids came into general usage, in the form of mobile cranes, fork-lift trucks, saddle carriers and side-loaders.

ABOVE: A deal carrier at work, hurrying along a narrow plank high above the ground.

LEFT: Deals being piled in Romans yard beside Llanthony Warehouse c.1925.
ENGLISH HERITAGE NMR

BELOW: Nicks & Co., timber importers, advertisement from a Gloucester guide c.1950. The company are still in business.

Established 1855

NICKS & COMPANY
Timber Importers

SOFTWOODS : HARDWOODS : PLYWOOD : WALLBOARDS

Sawing, Planing and Moulding Mills : Joiners

—

Canada Wharf, Bristol Road
GLOUCESTER

Telegrams : NICKS   Telephone No. : 28231

Dock Labourers

BELOW: Dockers on the North Quay in the 1920s.
THE WATERWAYS TRUST

BOTTOM: Corn porters with their sack trucks, c.1900.

The labourers in the docks needed strength and stamina to cope with the hard work involved in handling cargoes with few mechanical aids. Much was piece-work, with gangs of men being paid to complete a particular task and all members of the gang were expected to pull their weight. Their times of work were signalled by the bell on the corner of the North Warehouse.

Some dock labourers worked regularly for specific merchants and the corn merchants J. & C. Sturge had a reputation for looking after their employees. They built houses for some of their key workers and they organised an annual Christmas tea party, which was followed by speeches about such worthy matters as temperance and education. During the trade depression caused by the Crimean War, they even provided work for their men, whitewashing the inside of their empty warehouses.

Labourers who discharged cargo from a ship (later known as dockers) were employed on a casual basis each day. Men looking for work assembled each morning, the names of those chosen were called out by the stevedore who was managing the discharge and the remainder returned home empty handed. The demand for this casual labour was very variable, as it was determined by the quantities of goods being imported through the docks. The corn import trade depended very much on the size of the home harvest, whilst the timber trade was seasonal because the exporting ports were iced-up during the winter. Thus there were periods when good wages could be earned but also times of unemployment and distress.

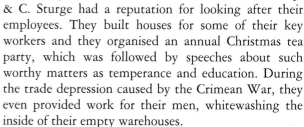

The toughness of the dock labourers stood them in good stead when a schooner loaded with oil cake for Foster Brothers tied up for the night at the quay opposite the mill and became trapped by ice. Rather than wait for the ice to thaw, the labourers laid bags on the ice and carried the heavy sacks across the canal to Foster Brothers' warehouse.

In the 20th century, the role of the dock labourers at Gloucester changed, as there were fewer seagoing ships to discharge but more barges and there was a gradual increase in mechanical aids. In the second half of the century, the number of labourers reduced steadily, and the last five dockers were made redundant in 1988.

Seamen

In the 19th century, many fine sailing ships delivered cargoes to Gloucester, bringing an ever-changing population of seamen to what was then a small inland county town. Most ships remained in port for a few weeks and although many seamen on British ships were paid off and left town, the master usually stayed on board and might be joined by his wife and sometimes his children, who travelled from their home to be with him. Seamen on foreign ships remained on board, helping to discharge the cargo and carry out minor maintenance tasks.

When the day's work was done, therefore, it was common to see seamen from many countries walking around town. Frenchmen were particularly noticeable, in clattering *sabots* and loose blue jerkins setting off with huge baskets to scour the country lanes in quest of edible snails. Other foreign seamen marched in groups, to seek entertainment and enjoyment at the numerous taverns in the area, some wearing bright sashes, top boots and *bandalero* hats. They did not have far to march, as there was over a dozen public/beer houses in the streets immediately surrounding the docks and many landlords were prepared to bend the licensing laws.

Inevitably, some of these evening outings culminated in distressing incidents. Local newspapers carried many reports of seamen involved in fights, robberies or accidents. For minor offences, charges were not always proceeded with, as the magistrates were prepared to accept assurances from the accused or from his captain that he would soon be leaving port. More serious cases were committed to the assizes in the usual way. Some evenings ended with a seaman under the influence of drink falling into the dock and drowning. On the way back to their ship, seamen had to pick their way over the ropes criss-crossing the quays and clamber over other vessels before reaching their own and it is hardly surprising that some ended up in the water. If a seaman was missing, an underwater search was made using the drags – a triangular iron frame with three hooks that was dragged along the bottom of the dock on the end of a long rope.

By the beginning of the 20th century, the number of seamen visiting Gloucester had declined significantly as the increased size of ship then in common service needed to discharge cargo at Sharpness.

ABOVE: A detail from an early engraving of the docks, c. 1840.

BELOW: Seamen furling sails during the Gloucester Tall Ships Festival 2007.

Boatmen

ABOVE: *Narrow boats being loaded with grain on the East Quay c.1900.*
NEIL PARKHOUSE

BELOW: *Severn & Canal Carrying Co. boatmen pose on their canal boats in Gloucester Lock in the 1920s.*
THE WATERWAYS TRUST

Many local men worked on the narrow canal boats that went 'up country' carrying cargoes to and from the Midlands. In the early days, most carried grain, timber or hay up the river and returned with coal or salt. The majority of owners had just one or two boats and few had more than four. Many owners were local coal merchants or owner-boatmen supplying coal merchants and some were local corn or timber merchants. A few owners had larger fleets that normally carried mixed cargoes, known as sundries.

The majority of Gloucester boatmen had their own home and only lived on the boat while on a trip. Some boats were worked by two men but as the master was paid a sum for the trip, it made sense to take members of his family when practical. Masters with young children were likely to take the whole family on the boat but once the eldest son was about ten years old, just he would go with his father, leaving mother at home with the younger children. One consequence was that boat children developed the skills to be boatmen in later life and did not get much schooling for any other occupation.

By the end of the 19th century, the number of small owners had declined, but the Severn & Canal Carrying Co. had over seventy boats carrying a wide range of general cargoes. They also had a fleet of barges trading between Gloucester and ports in the Bristol Channel, and Biddle Warehouse on the corner of the Barge Arm became the main centre for transhipment between barge and boat. Most of the boats went up to Birmingham but some went further to Wolverhampton or Walsall. The round trip commonly took 10 to 15 days and on arrival at Gloucester, the crew returned to their homes to wait until it was their turn to set off again.

Some trips involved first going down the canal to Cadbury's factory at Frampton to collect a raw form of chocolate (known as crumb) to be taken to Bournville near Birmingham for refining. While this was being loaded, it was not unknown for a bag to be 'accidentally' damaged and boatmen usually had a supply to hand out to children on their trips 'up country'. By the 1930s, some motor boats were in service but boat traffic largely died out in the 1950s.

Bargemen

Gloucester men also worked on the barges trading down to the Bristol Channel ports and up the river to Worcester and Stourport. In the 19th century, these carried a wide range of general cargoes in each direction, whilst in the 20th century, there were additional barges carrying bulk cargoes inland and returning empty. By the 1930s, some motor barges were in service and a workshop was established beside the Barge Arm for servicing the engines of both barges and boats. Other local men worked on lighters bringing grain and timber from Sharpness to Gloucester, with some continuing up the river. In the 1930s, a new group of bargemen emerged to crew a growing fleet of tanker barges, bringing petroleum products to depots at Monk Meadow Dock and places up river. Some of these men were recruited from the boatmen but there was also an influx of new men from Yorkshire, who brought barges around the coast from Knottingley. The barges and lighters remained busy well into the 1960s but then declined rapidly.

ABOVE: The Severn & Canal Carrying Co's base on the corner of the Barge Arm, where cargoes were transferred between barges and narrow canal boats.

LEFT: Heavy sacks being transferred from a barge to a narrow canal boat in the Barge Arm in the 1930s. When a loaded barge arrived at Gloucester, the boatman who was next 'on turn' brought his boat alongside and as the goods were transferred by the derrick (or the crane around the corner), he was responsible for stowing them to ensure that the boat was properly trimmed. Once the boat was loaded, the steerer went to the office to pick up the cargo papers and his starting money, and then moved his boat across the dock to be ready for an early departure in the morning.
ENGLISH HERITAGE NMR

A New Era

ABOVE: The MARQUES taking part in filming for a German television programme in 1982.

BELOW: The Port 400 festival in 1980 demonstrated the potential for future leisure activities in the docks.

By the 1970s, commercial traffic using the canal was at a low ebb. A few coasters used the quays below Llanthony Bridge but the size of ship that could pass along the canal was barely economic. Barge traffic to Gloucester ended when Reynolds Mill closed in 1977 and the City Flour Mills was supplied by road, although two barges still regularly passed through Gloucester carrying wheat to Healing's Mill at Tewkesbury. Some of the large warehouses were partly in use but most were standing empty and the front of the North Warehouse was propped up with scaffolding. There was a modest growth in pleasure craft using the canal but the dock estate was enclosed and visitors were not encouraged. One good consequence of the low level of activity, however, was that the docks made an ideal setting for filming scenes for period feature films and television series, such as 'The Onedin Line'.

Recognising that a major change of direction was needed, British Waterways, who owned the dock estate, published a study in 1976 of possible new uses for the docks and the surrounding buildings. This proposed the relocation of the remaining industrial uses and the redevelopment of the docks to provide a marina, housing, offices, an hotel and a theatre. No major developer came forward to take this scheme forward but it did pave the way for the Lock Warehouse to be converted to an Antiques Centre in 1979. In the following year, Gloucester Civic Trust and the local branch of the Inland Waterways Association tried to promote further action by organising a gathering of boats, land-based stalls, entertainments and refreshments. This was the first occasion on which the general public was encouraged to visit the docks and the popularity of the event demonstrated the potential for future leisure activities. Gloucester Civic Trust continued to raise public awareness by running regular guided tours of the docks.

In the following years, public access to the docks increased as more leisure-based activities were set up. Boat trips were available on the narrow boat *GLOSTER PACKET*. The Courtyard Arts Trust established a performance venue in the converted timber lighter *SEMINGTON*. Robert Opie opened an exhibition of retail packaging and advertising in the ground floor of the Albert Warehouse. The Alexandra Warehouse was refurbished for business and leisure uses, and the Pillar Warehouse on Bakers Quay was converted to offices, with a restaurant on the ground floor. The appearance of the docks was greatly enhanced in 1985 when the Square Sail company established a base for their tall ships, which were hired out for filming and were sometimes open to the public.

Keen to set an example of reusing more of the warehouses, Gloucester City Council purchased the North Warehouse for one pound and spent £1.5 million pounds converting

BELOW: The fire in the Britannia Warehouse in 1987 was a major setback for planned developments.

BOTTOM: EARL OF PEMBROKE in the large dry dock in 2006.

the building to house their main offices. Most of the roof had to be replaced but the main timbers were retained wherever possible. Any woodwork that had been affected by rot was cut away and replaced by short metal girders, and the former loading doors on each floor were replaced by windows. The restoration work, completed in July 1986, successfully provided a pleasant working environment for the Council staff, whilst still retaining the main features of the original warehouse. This helped to encourage Pearce Developments to put forward a major scheme for converting some of the other warehouses to offices or housing and building two large shopping malls to the east and south of the Victoria Dock. Before any work on this project could get under way, however, the Britannia Warehouse was seriously damaged by fire and there was a long delay while the future of the

remaining structure was debated. It was eventually decided that the ruin should be demolished and rebuilt with the external appearance similar to the original.

The Square Sail company left the docks in 1987 but their chief shipwright, Tommi Nielsen, stayed on to set up a company specialising in repairing and restoring traditional ships and their rigging. Using a combination of modern technology and the trusted techniques of the past, his craftsmen were soon attracting a wide variety of interesting vessels to Gloucester, including tall ships, Bristol Channel pilot cutters and even a replica Viking longboat.

Meanwhile, work was underway on the conversion of Llanthony

The National Waterways Museum was established in Llanthony Warehouse in 1988 and No. 4 steam dredger became a working exhibit.

Warehouse to house the National Waterways Museum in the lower floors, with offices above. The Museum was initially opened to the public on 1st April 1988 and the opening was celebrated by a visit from Prince Charles on 5th August. Also in 1988, the refurbishment of Herbert, Kimberley and Phillpotts warehouses was completed to provide more offices for Gloucester City Council. In the following year, the Merchants Quay shopping mall was opened to the south of Phillpotts Warehouse and a year later, the Soldiers of Gloucestershire Museum in the former Custom House reopened with an entrance from the docks.

Unfortunately, there then followed a long period of national economic difficulty, which inhibited further developments and no doubt contributed to the closure of the City Flour Mills in 1994 and the end of the grain barge traffic to Healing's Mill in 1998. Better times returned in the new century, when the South West Regional Development Agency began to provide quality paving and street furniture in the docks, and a national housing boom stimulated the conversion of the remaining warehouses to apartments and the construction of two new-build apartment projects. At the same time, Peel Developments and British Waterways began investing in the huge Gloucester Quays scheme to bring shops, housing, hotels, a college and leisure facilities to the area south of Llanthony Bridge. These investments opened the way for Gloucester Docks to have a new lease of life.

High Orchard Bridge at the centre of the Gloucester Quays project was raised for the first time on 25th January 2008 to allow PHOENIX to pass down the canal. The lifting span had been built on a temporary structure to the west of the canal and pushed into its proper position only a few days earlier.